My brother and sister have epilepsy

this is my story

Dr Richard Appleton LRCP, MRCS, MB BS, DCH, MA (Oxon), FRCP, FRCPCH
Consultant Paediatric Neurologist
Alder Hey Children's NHS Foundation Trust

Dr Annette Hames BA, MSc, PhD
Consultant Clinical Psychologist
Community Team Learning Disability

My brother and sister have epilepsy, this is my story

by Dr. Richard Appleton & Dr. Annette Hames

Illustrations by Phillip Bentley

Published in the UK by:

National Services for Health Improvement

Nucleus@The Bridge

London Science and Business Park

Brunel Way, Dartford DA1 5GA

Printed in the UK by Stephens & George Print Group

ISBN 978-0-9560921-3-7

About the authors

Richard Appleton is a full-time NHS consultant in Paediatric Neurology at Alder Hey Children's NHS Foundation Trust, Liverpool and Honorary Clinical Lecturer in Child Health, University of Liverpool, posts he has held since 1990. His specific interests within paediatric neurology include epilepsy, movement disorders and the rehabilitation of children who have experienced traumatic and non-traumatic brain injuries.

Richard has published a number of books on epilepsy and brain injuries for professionals, families and children. These include, 'Epilepsy and Your Child' (two editions), 'An Atlas of Epilepsy' (two editions), 'Epilepsy in Childhood and Adolescence' (three editions), 'Junior Encyclopaedia of Epilepsy' (book and CD), 'Hand in Hand: I have Epilepsy Too', 'Management of Brain Injured Children' (two editions), 'Epilepsy: the facts' (two editions) and 'Common Neurological Problems in General Paediatrics'. He has also co-designed, edited and contributed to four videos and CDs on the diagnosis and management of epilepsy in children and written a series of epilepsy syndrome factsheets for Epilepsy Action.

In addition, he is a professional adviser to 'Epilepsy Action' (the UK's leading charity for people with epilepsy), 'Epilepsy Bereaved' and the 'Tuberous Sclerosis Association'.

He is married to a paediatric occupational therapist and has three 'grown-up' children.

Annette Hames is a Consultant Clinical Psychologist with Northumberland Tyne and Wear NHS Trust. She has worked as a Clinical Psychologist with children with learning disabilities, and their families, for over 20 years in Newcastle upon Tyne. She has a particular interest in the experiences of siblings of children with learning disabilities and children with other chronic health conditions.

Her PhD *'Young children's understanding of learning disability'* compared siblings of children with learning disabilities and their peers, and identified that the siblings of children with disabilities have an enhanced ability to recognise abilities and disabilities in others. She has recently completed and published a 12-year study which followed the developing understanding of disability amongst a small group of siblings, and has co-authored *'Special brothers and sisters. Stories and tips for siblings of children with a disability or serious illness'* and *'Handling Haemophilia. Siblings' points of view'* for the Haemophilia Society. She lives in Newcastle with her husband and three teenage children.

Introduction

A number of healthy siblings (brothers and sisters) of children with disabilities and chronic illnesses, including the siblings of children with epilepsy, are at risk of having emotional and behavioural problems. These difficulties are more likely to occur if there is a poor knowledge of their brother or sister's illness. Parents are not always the best people to tell their children about a brother's or sister's illness. Sometimes they will over-estimate what siblings know about the illness. At other times they may keep the information to themselves. This may make it very difficult for siblings to understand, and as a result, they may not know how to help their brother or sister who has epilepsy.

One way to provide information has been by personal stories written by siblings. This is because these stories may be 'more real', and therefore more relevant and useful, than the information received from adults. We feel that it could be particularly helpful for siblings, if they feel that they have responsibilities for their brothers and sisters, to hear about others' experiences.

We have spoken to families who have been to the paediatric neurology and epilepsy clinics at Alder Hey Children's Hospital (Liverpool) and Newcastle General Hospital. Some of the children in these families have been asked if they would be happy to write a story about what it is like to live with a brother or sister with epilepsy. The stories in this booklet have been written by the siblings in these families. We have been delighted with how honest and truthful these young people have been in sharing their feelings with others. They have talked about the difficulties, anxieties and responsibilities that they have often felt. However, they have also told us how much they love their brothers and sisters, and how they 'would not change them for the world'.

We hope that all siblings who read this booklet will be able to recognise some of their own feelings in the stories. We also hope that that the stories will be useful in helping them to understand that there are many other brothers and sisters out there with very similar experiences. Finally, we think that parents and doctors and nurses will also find these stories helpful.

our stories

Elizabeth's story

Elizabeth is 8 years old and is the sister of James who is 5 and has epilepsy, as well as severe learning and physical disabilities

My brother James is nice to play with, he laughs when I clap my hands and sing happy birthday to him. He likes to play with baby card books, watching the washing machine on spin, and he loves Bear in the big blue house videos. I do not mind that he has it on a lot, I just play with my dolls. I love to hug and tickle my brother, it makes me laugh. I get scared when he has a fit and has to go to hospital.

When we go out, James shouts, does raspberries and his very own duck noise. Some people stare and some people say what lovely curly hair he has. I am not too keen on the people who stare because it's rude and a bit mean. I like to see people talking to my brother, he cannot talk, but they make him laugh.

I love my brother very much.

When we go out, James shouts, does raspberries

and his very own duck noise

About Elizabeth's story

It can be a little hard if people stare at your brother or sister. Tell your parents if you do not like it. They will be able to help you understand why people do stare.

Laura's story

Laura is 9 years old and is sister to Sammie, who is 2½

My brother Sammie has a mixture of nocturnal epilepsy, speech and language difficulties and autistic traits.

Sammie is a pain but we know he can't help it. Here are some of the things he does: he smashes vases and mugs, smacks, screams, hogs the TV, throws cars at the TV, puts things on the fire, throws the rats, guinea pig and rabbits and smacks the dog and basically things like that. If Sammie does something naughty we try not to get cross and shout. We also have problems making him understand what we mean. He can't talk very well, he makes lots of attempts, and I'm getting quite good at understanding him, for example 'Bop Bop' means he wants Mummy.

Sammie does not eat very much, he will occasionally eat sausage, toast, chocolate and pink doughnuts (and only pink).

My brother has no sense of danger and once he was running towards a deep lake, my granddad ran and hurt his leg trying to stop him (luckily he did).

That's our little monkey Sammie

Laura's story

My mum and I desperately wanted some time together and one Sunday we went shopping and about two weeks later my brother went to the Sea Life Centre with my uncle, aunt and my cousin Jack, and my mum stayed after my dance exam and played Monopoly while Dad was at work.

We even put locks on the bathrooms and my bedroom because he gets everything out of my draws and usually breaks them. In the bathroom he puts things down the toilet and flushes it.

Sammie does not sleep and he keeps Mummy up most of the night, she gets tired and grouchy. Sometimes she gets cross with me because she is so tired, but I know she doesn't mean to and loves me lots.

Sometimes we wish Sammie would behave long enough for us to go out as a family. Despite him being a huge pain (with a capital P), I think he is cute and his difficulties don't stop him being part of the family. We love him for who he is although sometimes I'd quite happily swap him for a quieter brother (or even a tortoise) who didn't want so much of mummy's time and attention.

That's our little monkey Sammie.

About Laura's story

Some, but not all, children with epilepsy can have difficulty falling asleep and staying asleep. When they wake up during the night, they will often wake their siblings up, as well as their parents. This can make everyone tired and bad-tempered. It is important to try and be as patient as possible – although this may not always be very easy!

Samantha is 10, and is sister to Harry, who is 7

When Harry's epilepsy first started I felt very sad and very worried about him. I hoped he wouldn't die, as I didn't understand at first. I cried a lot when I went to bed. I felt very lonely. I thought I was the only person who had a brother like Harry until I spoke to Anne Sweeney, Epilepsy Nurse Specialist. I started biting my nails a lot as I felt very anxious, as I did not know why he was having seizures.

Mum and Dad didn't tell me exactly what was happening to my brother as they didn't want to worry me. I wish they had told me more, or that I had someone else to talk to, someone who was going through the same feelings as me at the time, another child my age.

Maybe there should be an online chat room for children to talk over these things, share their feelings and help each other.

I thought I was the only person
who had a brother like Harry

Samantha's story

About Samantha's story

Siblings often feel sad and unhappy when their brother or sister is first diagnosed with epilepsy. Their parents may also be unhappy and upset and find it difficult to talk to their other children about epilepsy. However, it is important that you ask your parents about epilepsy and what it is. This will help you feel less sad about what is going on.

Connor's story

Connor is 10 and brother to Muir, 8, who has myoclonic epilepsy

About Muir

My brother Muir has epilepsy. He has had epilepsy since he was a baby. In the beginning it was very frightening. My mum used to call an ambulance and he was taken to hospital. Now we're all used to Muir's epilepsy, even though he has lots of seizures every week.

Muir can't speak very well and he likes to kiss anyone who is nice to him. My friends don't understand this and so I have to explain to them that Muir is a special boy who needs lots of looking after.

Now when we go on holiday we leave Muir at home with Inga our nanny. It's better that way. I know that Muir misses us, but holidays are too difficult for him. He doesn't like the sun and we have to keep him safe around the water.

I love Muir enormously. He makes me laugh. I help him with jigsaws and I build Brio trucks with him but he will always be a little boy even when I'm grown up.

He makes me laugh. I help him with jigsaws and
I build Brio trucks with him

Connor's story

About Connor's story

Fortunately, only a few families can't go on holiday together. Family holidays are usually more difficult to have when a brother's or sister's epilepsy is more difficult to control and the seizures are happening very frequently. Sometimes family holidays will have to be 'put on hold' or delayed until after the brother's or sister's epilepsy has come under better control.

Niall is 10, brother to Lewis, 15

The last fit that I can remember Lewis having was about two years ago. My mam was going out and me and Lewis were sleeping at our nanna's. My brother said that he didn't feel well and started shaking and throwing up. I asked my nanna if I could ring my mam and she said no because she thought it was just going to happen the once. But he kept throwing up, so I phoned my mam. I was crying a bit because he wouldn't stop being sick. I told my mam that Lewis was in a fit, and that he kept shaking. My mam came and got him and put him to bed in our house and then rang the hospital and they sent an ambulance. My mam then rang my nanna so she could come and look after me while my brother was in hospital. He had to go because he couldn't even stand.

I only just saw little shakes before that. I knew what it was because my mam had always said watch out for Lewis in case he has a fit. He will start shaking and staring at stuff for a while. Since then I have known what to look out for. I am glad that my mam told me. I worry less now that I know, because I know what to do. If he was sitting at a table and started staring at something then I would move everything away, like his knife and his folk and his cup. I would also tell my mam or whoever was there. I hadn't really worried about it before, because although my mam told me, I thought it wouldn't happen.

I don't really notice the little fits. Sometimes when he is in his bedroom I look in and he is sitting there and he is staring at the floor or the window and I ask him what it is and he says 'I am having a fit', though it might not be anything. Now it is quite normal for him to have them. Though I don't really think about it much.

I made a speech in school this year about Lewis

I made a speech in school this year about Lewis. I was going to do one about football but my mam told me to do something different, so I did it about Lewis. I said that he was 15 years old, and that he had a condition called Tuberous Sclerosis. I said that meant that he could do magnificent things like he was lucky to go on a trip to Old Trafford and was once the mascot for Newcastle United. But although he can't read or write he can manage to pick his teams on the playstation from the flags and the badges. When I was making my speech I felt a few tears in my eyes. Now people in my class know about him and they don't ask about him.

If I described him, I would say he is nice but horrible sometimes. He would say the same about me. I miss him when he is away at respite. I miss the fighting!

About Niall's story

It is always best to talk to people such as your friends and family about having a brother or sister with epilepsy. This is not always easy but it is important to do it because it helps to tell others all about epilepsy. It is surprising how little people know about epilepsy. Some adults and children have very strange ideas about epilepsy and this can make them afraid about the condition. Once they know the facts about epilepsy they often stop being frightened or worried.

Lindsay's story

Lindsay is 12, and is sister to Graeme, 15, who has polymicrogyria and pachygyria

When my friends ask me, I tell them about epilepsy. It is hard to explain it. I explain how he has fits and what they are. My friends ask, but if they have never seen one it is hard to explain. I tell them before he has one because I once had a friend who got scared when he had one and she didn't know what it was. So I normally tell them. I tell them he has had epilepsy since he was born, and that he gets worse as he gets older. My friends don't worry, because it's the same friends who always come over. They have seen quite a few fits and they normally carry on, and don't think anything of it because they have seen it before.

He has lots every day, lots and lots. Sometimes we don't even know that he is having them. He has seven or eight different types of fits. My mum knows all their names. I don't really worry, but I do when he falls down, because he hurts his leg and breaks his leg, and then he won't be able to walk. One leg has broken about six times and the other he has broken twice. You can't really stop him because he is so big now. He is 15, nearly 16. He falls on top of you. If he is sitting on the sofa then he is safe, but if he is standing then I am frightened in case he falls again.

It was less of a worry when he was younger because he was more able bodied. He used to run and kick a football. He is getting worse as he gets older. He used to be able to run around, but now you have to hold his hand. He is in a wheelchair a lot of the time. He walks round the house and at school. But he has got to walk to strengthen his bones, and he goes swimming at school, to strengthen his legs. He has got a bike, and he never used to be able to ride, but he can do it now on his own. He is a bit wild, he rams into bushes. He only does it because my dad has to go in and get him back out again. I used to do more things with him when we were little, like go outside, but not now. I go out on my bike with him sometimes when my dad is with him, but not often.

He has got a really naughty character. If I go to help him with his DVD, he starts hitting me for no reason. He follows my mum and dad all the time, he walks behind them, but he needs someone to help him. He wants to follow my mum, because he doesn't want to be on his own. Someone has to sit with him, and when my Nana is here she does, so that my mum and dad can get on with their jobs. It is difficult for my mum and dad to get on with jobs. I sit with him sometimes, and shout for my mum if he tries to get up. If people are coming to see him, I tell him that they won't come if he gets up, and that stops him. Otherwise there is no real way to get him to sit down. If you just tell him, he will smack you. If he really hits me, I hit him back, but if it's only a little one I will leave it. He normally starts crying if I hit him, and then I tell my mum I didn't do anything. But sometimes we are both crying because he really nips me and hurts me. And sometimes he starts crying just because I started, so he is quite naughty. It is funny to talk about it afterwards. Though, when it actually happens it is not so funny.

I like him the way he is. I wouldn't change him for anything. Sometimes I say I would but I wouldn't.

I go out on my bike with him sometimes . . . he rams into bushes

About Lindsay's story

Graeme's epilepsy has been caused by a serious abnormality of the brain called 'polymicrogyria' and 'pachygyria'. These two medical words mean that his brain was made abnormally before he was born.

Lindsay has had quite a troublesome time with her brother, particularly after his epilepsy was diagnosed. This is because Graeme has many different types of epileptic seizures and most have been difficult to control. He also has difficulty looking after himself and can be naughty. Lindsay feels responsible for looking after her brother when her parents are busy, and this can make her feel unhappy. Fortunately, most children with epilepsy do not have the problems that Graeme has. Lindsay also explains how it is helpful if siblings tell their friends about epilepsy. There is a lot of research that shows that if people understand something unusual, they are less likely to get upset by it or scared by it. It may be a good idea to tell friends about epilepsy, even before they see a brother or sister have an epileptic fit.

William's story

William is 12, brother of Patrick 10, who has Landau Kleffner Syndrome

My name is William. I have two sisters and a brother who has Landau Kleffner Syndrome, which includes having epilepsy and communication problems. I think my siblings and I are the main pushing power of his confidence to go to school, and live his life in a way that any other kid does.

My brother is the youngest in our family, so he looks up to me and does the things I do. So I have to be careful, as does any family with a special needs kid. I find it so hard to communicate with my brother because he knows something is wrong with him, which he wants to change, but can't. Also the stress it brings to your parents is so apparent, in the way their daily routine is shattered by their mind set of getting the best for their kids, but still making sure that the child with the problem is on their minds 24/7.

My brother is the youngest in our family,
so he looks up to me and does the things I do

William's story

About William's story

Many brothers and sisters feel responsible for helping to care for and look after their sibling who has epilepsy. This may be because they are simply that sort of person and want to help. However, it may also be because they want to help their parents as they can see how stressed and tired they can become. They should talk to their parents about this, if this is how they feel. Their parents will probably remind them that it is they who are responsible for their child with epilepsy, and not their brothers and sisters.

Rosanna's story

Rosanna is 13, and is sister of Patrick, 10, who has Landau Kleffner Syndrome

I am 13. I live with my mum, dad, older sister and two younger brothers. My youngest brother, Patrick, has something called Landau Kleffner Syndrome (LKS). We first knew he had it when he was 7.

LKS means that Tosh (we call Patrick Tosh at home) has epilepsy, central deafness and speech problems. I feel upset because he is not as fortunate as me or my brother and sister. I get quite annoyed because Mum and Dad buy Tosh lots of toys to keep him happy about all of his doctor's appointments etc.

I feel Mum and Dad are sometimes too involved with Tosh to give us some attention. For instance they bought him a dog (we already have two dogs and one cat) to help Tosh and give him a friend. I think Monty has helped Tosh a lot as he finds it difficult to make friends and most of his friends are either younger or older than him. Some kids find it hard to understand Tosh's condition. He often takes a long time to say something or appears to be ignoring you, when actually it is that he hasn't understood you. Then they become impatient with Tosh and that makes me feel sad.

He also needs a lot of help with his homework,
I help quite a lot and enjoy it

He also needs a lot of help with his homework, I help quite a lot and enjoy it. Tosh's condition has made me more aware and I would like to help kids with special needs when I am older. I know it can be a challenge but I think it is very rewarding too.

Rosanna's story

About Rosanna's story

It's important that siblings do not feel that their brother or sister with epilepsy is spoilt. If siblings feel like this, they should talk to their parents about what they think they are doing. It's very important that brothers and sisters feel that they are treated fairly and equally.

Amy's story

Amy is 14, sister of George, 7, who has a severe form of epilepsy called epidermal naevus syndrome

"Life with George"

It is hard to write about life with George as it is 'normal' day to day life living with George and his epilepsy. George, as well as epilepsy has many other problems, but epilepsy is the main one that affects him and the family most. Despite this he is a happy boy and on a good day, where he has maybe four or five fits, he is happy in himself and likes to walk around and play. On a bad day, he can have up to and over one an hour. He tends to be cuddly and they can knock him off his feet. George has had epilepsy since he was born and has always had fits daily.

When he was younger his fits were a lot different to what they are now. His fits used to mean that he was sick on a regular basis. These were very hard to deal with. It meant that when we would go out we would have to ensure that we had a spare set of clothes for him and a towel that we could try and catch the sick in. It would sometimes take two or three attempts to leave the house. To do something as simple as going for a walk down the prom was made difficult.

To do something as simple as going for a walk down the prom was made difficult

As George has changed and grown, so have his fits. He now has some that are hard to notice unless you know him and know what you are looking for. Others he will drop to the floor and his whole body will become stiff. I wouldn't say that these are easier to cope with, but they do mean that my sister and I can deal with them on our own and do not have to ask Mum and Dad, or each other for help.

I would never change George and I don't resent him for my life being different to my friends. I always ask my mum if there is anything that she needs me to do before I go out or when I come in. We all pull together as a family, working together when looking after George. My sister and I have set routines in the morning before school where we change who watches him at certain times so we can all get ready.

Our mum and dad try to let us lead as 'normal' a life as possible, by still going on holiday and going for days out together. But at the end of the day this is normal for us as we have never had a different George or a different life and would never want one.

People will never understand how you feel and what your life is like unless they go through it themselves. What matters is you love this person and you do everything you can to help them. It is hard and it may never become easy, but we cope.

About Amy's story

We all get used to leading different lives, and we assume that the lives we lead are normal. Many children say that they would not want to change their lives, nor would they want to change their brother or their sister, even with all the demands that they make or problems they cause. To change them would be to have a different brother or sister, which is something that they do not want.

Lucia is 15, sister of Patrick, 10, who has Landau Kleffner Syndrome

I am 15, the oldest of the four children. I have one sister aged 13, a younger brother aged 12, and my youngest brother who is 10. My youngest brother has a condition called Landau Kleffner Syndrome (LKS). This is a type of epilepsy but it also affects my brother's speech and understanding. Because my brother's speech and language is affected by his condition, the whole family took up sign language and found this a useful experience, not just because it helped my brother, but because knowing sign language could become more useful later in life.

One of the scariest times that I will always remember was one night when I was up late in my room doing homework, I heard my brother yelling in his room. I went in and he was having an epileptic fit. I was really scared and called my parents who helped him and gave him medicine, but that really upset and frightened me.

At home I think my parents do try to make sure that all four of us are treated fairly but as my brother needs more help it does

Because my brother's speech and language is
affected by his condition, the whole family
took up sign language

become difficult. I think that sometimes my other two siblings do feel that he is favoured and this frustrates them and can cause arguments. I feel sad that my brother has LKS because he won't be able to do some of the things that he wants to do in the future and I can see that he finds it frustrating to communicate sometimes. But I think that in general our family have dealt with my brother and his condition well.

About Lucia's story

It can be a really good idea for other members of the family to learn sign language. This can be a clever skill to teach friends at school. It can also be a useful skill to have when you want to communicate with somebody else, and don't want others to know what you are saying. Many siblings say that they are grateful to their brothers and sisters for having taught them how to use sign language.

Gemma's story

Gemma is 16, sister of George, aged 7

"Do you need me to watch George?"

George has had epilepsy since he was born. Since then 'Do you need me to watch George' is the phrase you hear most often in our house. With George having epilepsy he needs to be watched constantly, this can sometimes limit what you can do. As George has been here as long as I can remember, I have got used to it, it seems normal to me. Unlike my friends who can drop everything and go out, I cannot, and unless I think about it, I don't really notice.

As well as epilepsy George has other problems. He is deaf in one ear and blind in one eye, he has lots of marks on his skin and may never be able to talk. George has not got a mild case of epilepsy, his is very complicated. He can have between 4 and 7 fits on a normal day and a lot more on others, each fit can look different. It is not weird to me as I don't know any different.

A long time ago when George was really ill, it was much harder. Because of his epilepsy and other problems, one person would have to watch him, with someone else near just in case something went wrong. It was at a stage that after every meal he would be sick because of his medication.

Before George we went on big holidays abroad, but not as much now. We still go on holidays abroad but nearer to home so George doesn't have to travel far on a plane. It is a bit weird though, when my friends brag about going to cool places like Canada, Australia, New York or Japan, and I say I went to Spain, although it doesn't bother me.

It is fun to spend time with him, and it is great to see him learn new things like learning to swim

Gemma's story

There is more than one side to having a sibling with epilepsy. Whereas most brothers and sisters don't get along with their sibling, with me and George this isn't the case. We don't fight because George cannot. George having problems limits me, it's daft but having epilepsy makes him a much better brother. I play with him all the time, not because I have to, but because I want to. With not knowing how long he will be here, I like to spend time with him a lot. I sometimes forget about his problems because of his character; he is funny and stubborn, apart from his problems he is just like a regular little brother. It is fun to spend time with him, and it is great to see him learn new things like learning to swim and other things, as he is only seven. Some people won't understand this but they would if they had a sibling with epilepsy. The bottom line is that him having epilepsy doesn't make you love him less, I think it makes you love him more and I wouldn't swap him for the world.

About Gemma's story

It's very common for siblings to say that having a brother or sister with epilepsy means that they get on with them better. Lots of brothers and sisters may dislike or even say that they 'hate' each other and fight constantly, whereas siblings of children with disabilities often get on much better.

Michael's story

Michael is 16, and is brother to Rebekah, aged 3

My sister has got epilepsy. I am alright with it. Before she had medication, she had head drops frequently, she was in her own world a large amount of the time. That was two years ago. The medication stopped the epilepsy, stopped her head nods though it made her hyperactive, she has got endless amounts of energy. She wakes up at terrible times in the morning. My mum wakes up with her, I usually sleep through though she comes in and opens my door saying 'who's that?' She is frustrated a lot. It slows down her speech. She can only say 'mammy', 'daddy', 'hello' and 'hiya'. She is much better now. She picks up the phone and says 'hello'. Sometimes she says my name and sometimes she can't say my name. She's lost how to say it now. Every few months she can say it and then it comes back. I would love her to be able to say my name again. She calls my sister Charlie, 'Sarah', because her friend is called Sarah. She can't say my name. She has only said my name twice.

She is my little sister and I love her to bits because little sisters are always a pain in the backside. I am always cautious about going out, I will ask Mum, 'are you sure?' because a little extra help is everything. If I stay in she can have a cup of tea and recuperate. I am used to helping my mum. Sometimes other members of the family tell us what we should be doing with her and I get

She has her problems, but I'd not have her any other way

annoyed. I think you don't live here 24 hours a day. It is frustrating. They say what to do with her but they have got no idea. They tell me what to do. It's fair enough if my mum tells me what to do but they don't know what it's like.

Michael's story

She has got to be on medication for the rest of her life and continue on it forever. There is a possibility that she could grow out of it but she's too young to know. She has had scans and electrodes on her brain, she hates that and so do I. She doesn't like being touched around the head. I don't like seeing her in hospital even though it's for her own good. We have to restrain her. Mum does it, she has some strength and scratched my mum, and then I quickly help her, it's not very nice. When she has her medicine, she sits on her knee and we don't have to restrain her, just entertain her, and mum gives her medicine in a syringe. When she really doesn't want her medicine then we sing a song and that makes her happier.

Between the switch of medication, her whole head used to fall down and she wouldn't respond for 10 minutes. I had to keep a hold of her and eventually she fell asleep on me. And then as soon as she woke up she didn't want to let go because she felt safe and secure. It's not nice to see. I don't like to see her like that. I like to see her climbing in the garden and the soft play.

I have a lot of responsibility; I give my mum a break because she's up at 2am and up at 5:30 in the morning. I do jobs for Rebekah, like bathing her; I love bathing her and play outside with her in the jungle gym. I can't not be with her because she's everywhere. I am used to not having the attention because I'm the oldest in the family and I'm getting older.

Every fortnight a carer comes for a couple of hours and Mum has a good time. I don't go out with Mum much now. I occasionally go to the shops and we have a meal. It's nice to have time with Mum because she's always busy with Rebekah, in her bed, reading her books. When Rebekah is not there, she can talk but she's tired. I like having time with Mum. I go to my dad's at weekends, but that is when my mum has the most trouble with her. My concerns are that Mum is often on her own with Rebekah. She is totally drained. I wish she didn't have to work so hard and I hope she can cope, it's always in the back of my mind. I text her a lot when I am away. When she was pregnant with Rebekah I couldn't stop thinking about her when I was with my dad. She has always looked after us for such a long time.

It's really nice having another sister. At the start I didn't want one and then she came along and it was wonderful. She has her problems, but I'd not have her any other way. There are a lot worse diseases in the world. I love playing with her. If you are going to have a baby sister, they are going to take all the attention, young ones always do. It's a long hard ride at the start, but it's worth it.

Michael's story

About Michael's story

It can be worrying for siblings if their brothers and sisters are on a lot of medication, and as a result their behaviour is very difficult to manage. It is really important that siblings talk to parents and medical staff about what is happening to their brother or sister, and how the medication is helping. If they have worries about their brother or sister they must try and talk to someone about this, and try and find out how they can help. Also if they think something is not working, they need to try to discuss this too.

Michael tells us how much he cares for his mum and also that he understands how hard it is for her to cope with Rebekah's epilepsy. This is always more difficult when parents are not together so that they can share the work between them. In this situation brothers (like Michael), and sisters can provide a lot of help and support for their sibling and their mum or dad.

Stephen's story

Stephen is 18, and is brother to Anthony aged 7

Hi, my name is Stephen. After living with Anthony since he was born, you get used to the way he is. It is not easy at first and it took a while for it to sink in, but after a time you realise that epilepsy is going to be a part of his life, no matter what we as a family do for him. I wish I could do more for him, but I get scared that I might do more bad than good when he has a fit.

When Anthony was really bad, it affected all the family, nobody more than my mum. She tried to keep it to herself but I could tell she was really upset by the whole thing. Now things aren't that bad, Anthony still has fits but it is not as bad as it was a few years ago.

Would I change Anthony? This may sound strange to someone who hasn't met Anthony, but if you did meet him, you would know that he is a very happy boy with no worries and for that I am grateful.

he is a very happy boy
with no worries
and for that I am grateful

Stephen's story

About Stephen's story

Stephen reminds other siblings that although life might be difficult at first when you have a brother or sister with epilepsy, things usually get easier. It is not only that the family gets used to the epilepsy, but as the medication improves, the epilepsy is more likely to become stabilised and get better. The family also gets used to planning and using routines in the house which makes life much easier. Stephen's story is not unusual, and often siblings say that things get easier all the time.

Stephanie's story

Stephanie, 25, has a sister Annabel, who is 15 and has epilepsy

My name is Stephanie. I am 25 years old. My sister's name is Annabel. She is 15 years old. The name for my sister's medical condition is Epilepsy.

I was 10 years old when my mother and father told me they were going to have a baby. For 10 years I longed for a brother or sister and finally my dream had come true. When Annabel came along, she was beautiful … at last I had a sister! Three years later she became ill and tragically she was diagnosed with a brain tumour. Annabel had surgery on her brain to remove the tumour. She had a further 10 operations due to various complications she experienced on her road to recovery.

My parents were spending a lot of time at the hospital with my sister, so my auntie came to stay with me for a short while. I was 13 at the time and about to choose my GCSE options. With all of the pressure and stress my family and I were under, I began to feel increasingly uninterested in my schoolwork. Although I did not realise this at the time, I can now look back and understand the reasons for this. Everything felt so unfair and my mind was elsewhere, worrying about my sister and feeling upset all of the time. However, there were days when I put on a brave face in school and I would pretend to my friends that everything was ok.

For 10 years I longed for a brother or sister and finally my dream had come true

I felt nobody would understand what it was like to have a little sister who was so sick. I had nobody really to talk to about it and there was little help regarding information on dealing with things like this.

After many operations, Annabel had to learn how to do everything all over again. She had to learn how to walk, talk, feed and drink … everything! Gradually, with a lot of hard work from the staff at Walton Hospital and Alder Hey Children's Hospital, she began to slowly recover from her operations. Although I don't think she would have been able to recover so effectively if it wasn't for the help and support my parents gave her and of course, the determination of Annabel herself.

Eventually, Annabel started mainstream school and she had two learning support assistants to help with her work. Annabel still had a balance problem and needed some help in getting around but she was cheerful and polite and she took part in all of the activities she could. We encouraged her to live life to the full and do the same things all of the other children would do. It was important to not treat her differently because she had a disability. Annabel met new friends who looked after her and were very understanding and patient towards her. Annabel loved school and she was very happy. A few years later, when Annabel was eight years old, she developed epilepsy. She developed this due to the brain surgery she had when she was three. I remember feeling confused by this happening and couldn't believe why something else had to happen to her. Hadn't she been through enough?

Today, Annabel is 15 years old and has lived with epilepsy for seven years. She attends mainstream secondary school and is taking her GCSEs. Annabel still has a full time learning support assistant who helps with her school work.

Although Annabel has epilepsy, my parents and I encourage her to take part in regular activities such as drama and swimming. She has done so well in dealing with her problems and has received many awards for her determination and hard work through all of this.

Having a sister with epilepsy is upsetting at times, but we have to stay strong and get on with our lives as best as possible. When things seem a little dull, I always look on the bright side and remember that there are lots of people in the world who are going through worse situations and we should count ourselves lucky for the things that we have got. I also remember how we were once told Annabel might never walk or talk again and at one point the doctors said she might be blind. Again, when things seem dull, I always look at her and think 'WOW, look how grown up she looks and how well she has recovered'.

Annabel can walk, talk and even swim. She can do most things teenagers can do. So when I think of the nice things and the things that she can do, life seems a little brighter again. However, my parents and I do have to keep a careful eye on her when she is swimming and walking up and down stairs, but this has just become a way of life now and we have to accept that. Annabel is most of the time unaware that we watch her carefully, as we try not to make this too obvious to her. We always encourage her to take part in activities and on a couple of occasions she has been to Liverpool City Centre, shopping with her best friend. It is important for her to gain her independence as she gets older, so there are times when you have to let go and allow her to grow and develop. It is worrying but we feel it is good for Annabel to learn how to do things for herself and not depend on others for help all of the time.

Annabel is a lovely person. She is friendly, kind and loving. There is always some hope that one day her epilepsy will just go away but even if it doesn't, I will always be there for my sister, no matter what. That's what a strong family is all about, being there for one another and getting through what life throws at you together. You have to make the best of any situation and look at the positive things in life rather than the negative. That always helps.

About Stephanie's story

Stephanie's story highlights how important it is to have people to talk to. Especially when siblings are doing exams it is important that their other worries are discussed so that they can concentrate on their work.

Stephanie also reminds us that there is a light at the end of the tunnel. When you look back you can see how far your brother or sister has come. Any achievements are so wonderful to see. It is a good idea to look back and see the big steps that your brother or sister has made.

bye!

Notes